Piano Exam Pieces

ABRSM Grade 3

Selected from the 2017 & 2018 syllabus

C000126891

Name

Date of exam

Contents

Editor for ABRSM: Richard Jones

CD				page
	LIST A			
1	1	**George Frideric Handel** Sonatina in G, HWV 582		2
2	2	**Wolfgang Amadeus Mozart** Romanze (from *Eine kleine Nachtmusik*, K. 525, second movement), arr. Clem Virgo		3
3	3	**Ludwig van Beethoven** German Dance in B flat: No. 6 from 12 German Dances, WoO 13		4
	LIST B			
7	1	**Charles Dibdin** Tom Bowling, arr. Julian McNamara		5
8	2	**Ferdinand Hiller** Polnisches Lied: No. 18 from *Leichte Lieder und Tänze*, Op. 117		6
9	3	**Pyotr Il'yich Tchaikovsky** Marche des soldats de bois: No. 5 from *Album pour enfants*, Op. 39		8
	LIST C			
13	1	**Dmitry Borisovich Kabalevsky** Clowns: No. 20 from *24 Easy Pieces*, Op. 39		10
14	2	**Nikolay Petrovich Rakov** Der Tag ist vergangen: No. 24 from *Aus Jugendtagen*		11
15	3	**Nicholas Scott-Burt** Attitude!		12

Other pieces for Grade 3

LIST A

4	4	**J. S. Bach** Bourrée: 5th movt from Overture in F, BWV 820. No. 45 from *Baroque Keyboard Pieces*, Book 1 (ABRSM) or No. 5 from *A Keyboard Anthology*, 2nd Series, Book 1 (ABRSM)
5	5	**Mozart** Menuett in F (Menuett 2 from K. 6). No. 42 from L. Mozart, *Notebook for Nannerl* (Schott) or No. 2 from Mozart, *Easy Piano Pieces and Dances* (Bärenreiter)
6	6	**Trad. English** Staines Morris. No. 28 from *English Folk Tunes for Piano*, arr. Carson Turner (Schott)

LIST B

10	4	**Burgmüller** Angelic Harmony: No. 21 from *25 Easy and Progressive Studies*, Op. 100 (ABRSM)
11	5	**Carroll** Dwarfs of the Mist: No. 8 from *Forest Fantasies* (Forsyth)
12	6	**Saint-Saëns** L'éléphant, arr. Heumann. *Encore*, Book 2 (ABRSM)

LIST C

16	4	**Hywel Davies** Adieu. *Folk Roots for Piano*, arr. Davies (Boosey & Hawkes)
17	5	**Trad. Spiritual** Swing low, sweet chariot, arr. Richards. *Piano Mix 3* (ABRSM)
18	6	**Sarah Watts** Curtain Call. Sarah Watts, *Shades of Blue* (Kevin Mayhew) or Sarah Watts, *Razzamajazz Repertoire Piano* (Kevin Mayhew)

First published in 2016 by ABRSM (Publishing) Ltd,
a wholly owned subsidiary of ABRSM, 24 Portland Place,
London W1B 1LU, United Kingdom
© 2016 by The Associated Board of the Royal Schools of Music
Distributed worldwide by Oxford University Press

Music origination by Julia Bovee
Cover by Kate Benjamin & Andy Potts
Printed in England by Halstan & Co. Ltd, Amersham,
Bucks., on materials from sustainable sources.

A:1

Sonatina in G

HWV 582

G. F. Handel
(1685–1759)

This is a contrapuntal piece in two parts; its double theme is exchanged between the hands in the first two bars. Handel wrote it in London around 1722, presumably for teaching purposes. In this edition, all slurs and dynamics are editorial suggestions only, as is the trill at the final cadence. In the source, the seventh bass note of b. 5 is *g*, but it has been corrected here to *e* in accordance with bb. 7 and 16.
Sources: autograph MS, Cambridge, Fitzwilliam Museum, MS 263; MS copy, London, British Library, R.M. 18.b.8.

© 2016 by The Associated Board of the Royal Schools of Music

Romanze

from *Eine kleine Nachtmusik*, K. 525, second movement

A:2

Arranged by Clem Virgo

W. A. Mozart
(1756–91)

This piece is the slow movement of Mozart's *Eine kleine Nachtmusik* (A Little Night Music), probably his most popular and best loved instrumental work. He composed it in the summer of 1787, while working on his opera *Don Giovanni*. Written for string quartet and double bass, it belongs to a type of entertainment music called *notturno* (nocturne), intended for performance at night.

The vocal 'romance' genre is here imitated in a slow movement of simple, lyrical character. It is in ABA song form, but only the A section is given here. Quaver pairs (bb. 3, 6 and 14–15) might be played (the original string version has). The only exception is the quaver pair at the beginning of b. 7, which should be played as written.

German Dance in B flat

No. 6 from 12 German Dances, WoO 13

Ludwig van Beethoven
(1770–1827)

A German Dance is a dance for couples in quick triple time, popular in South Germany and Austria in the late 18th and early 19th centuries. Haydn, Mozart, Beethoven and Schubert all wrote many sets of such pieces.

The original orchestral versions of Beethoven's *12 deutsche Tänze*, WoO 13, which no longer survive, belong to his early period in Vienna (1792–1802). They were written for public, social occasions, whereas the later (*c.*1800) authentic piano arrangements, which still exist, were intended for private use in the home. In No. 6, reproduced here, the lower-stave slurs in bb. 10, 18, 26, 28 and 30, and the upper-stave slurs in bb. 27–30 are editorial, as is the opening dynamic mark.

Sources: Staatsbibliothek zu Berlin, Preußischer Kulturbesitz, MS Artaria 137; 1st edition, ed. O. E. Deutsch (Vienna: Strache, 1929)

Tom Bowling

B:1

Arranged by Julian McNamara

Charles Dibdin
(1745–1814)

Charles Dibdin was the most prolific English songwriter of his day, composing over 600 songs. He also wrote many stage works (operas, operettas, pantomimes, etc.) for the London theatres. 'Tom Bowling' – the words and music of which are both by Dibdin – was written on the death of his eldest brother Thomas, who was captain of a ship in the East India trade and died at sea. The first verse begins as follows:

> Here, a sheer hulk, lies poor Tom Bowling, the darling of our crew;
> No more he'll hear the tempest howling, for death has broached him to.

Some people will be familiar with the melody from its use in the fourth movement of Sir Henry Wood's *Fantasia on British Sea Songs*, which used to be played regularly on the last night of the BBC Proms.

Polish Song

Polnisches Lied

No. 18 from *Leichte Lieder und Tänze*, Op. 117

Edited by Lionel Salter

Ferdinand Hiller
(1811–85)

B:2

This haunting piece has the character of a traditional folk dance. The 12-bar melody is first played in a relatively simple harmonization, then (at b. 13) repeated with a more elaborate accompanying part. In the coda (b. 24), the first phrase of the melody moves to the bass and the accompanying part is in the treble.

Ferdinand Hiller was very active as a conductor in his native Germany, though he also spent some years in Paris and in Italy. His small piano pieces are still used for teaching purposes.

© 1990 by The Associated Board of the Royal Schools of Music
Reproduced from *More Romantic Pieces for Piano*, Book 1, edited by Lionel Salter (ABRSM)

B:3

Marche des soldats de bois

No. 5 from *Album pour enfants*, Op. 39

Edited by Howard Ferguson

P. I. Tchaikovsky
(1840–93)

Tchaikovsky's *Album pour enfants* (Album for the Young), Op. 39, was written in 1878 as a form of relaxation after the tremendous effort involved in composing his Fourth Symphony and the opera *Yevgeny Onegin*. The set was subtitled '24 Easy Pieces (à la Schumann)', which indicates that Tchaikovsky had in mind Schumann's *Kinderscenen* (Scenes from Childhood) and *Album für die Jugend* (Album for the Young).
Source: *Oeuvres complètes pour le piano, Vol. IV: nouvelle edition revue et corrigé par l'auteur* (Moscow: Jürgenson, 1893)

Клоуны Klouny

Clowns

No. 20 from *24 Easy Pieces*, Op. 39

D. B. Kabalevsky
(1904–87)

C:1

The Russian composer Dmitry Borisovich Kabalevsky studied piano and composition at the Moscow Conservatory, where he later taught, being appointed professor in 1939. He was active in the field of music education and wrote much music for children, notably the *24 Easy Pieces* (Легкие пьесы Legkie p'esy), Op. 39, from which 'Clowns' is selected. The quick, repeated change from major to minor in the theme perhaps reflects the 'laugh-cry' fooling about of the clown, who pretends he cannot decide whether to be happy or sad.

The Day is Ended

Der Tag ist vergangen

No. 24 from *Aus Jugendtagen*

C:2

N. P. Rakov
(1908–90)

This folksong-like piece conveys a feeling of sadness at the passing of day. Its Russian composer, Nikolay Petrovich Rakov, showed a special interest in music for children and wrote many piano pieces for teaching purposes, such as *Aus Jugendtagen* (From Days of Youth), from which this piece is selected. Rakov studied violin at the Rubinstein Music School and then composition with Glier at the Moscow Conservatory, where he later taught for many years.

C:3

Attitude!

Nicholas Scott-Burt
(born 1962)

Nicholas Scott-Burt is a composer, conductor, pianist and organist. He is also an ABRSM examiner and was awarded a PhD in composition from the University of Bristol in 2012. *Attitude!* is a short piece that he wrote for his youngest son, about which he has written: 'Attitudes can be good-tempered or bad-tempered – this is definitely the first sort! It should be played with a strong sense of purpose, sound a bit streetwise, but shouldn't forget its sense of humour!'

© 2016 by The Associated Board of the Royal Schools of Music